Other Books in The Far Side Series from Futura

Anthologies

Wildlife Preserves

A Far Side Collection

by Gary Larson

Futura

A Futura Book

Copyright © 1989 by Universal Press Syndicate

This edition published in 1990 by Futura Publications,
a Division of Macdonald & Co (Publishers) Ltd
London & Sydney

Reprinted 1990 (twice)

All characters in this publication are fictitious and any resemblance
to real persons, living or dead, is purely coincidental.

ISBN 0 7088 4558 4

Printed and bound in Great Britain by
The Guernsey Press Company Limited, Guernsey, Channel Islands

Futura Publications
A Division of
Macdonald & Co (Publishers) Ltd
Orbit House
1 New Fetter Lane
London EC4A 1AR

A Member of Maxwell Macmillan Pergamon Publishing Corporation

Wildlife Preserves

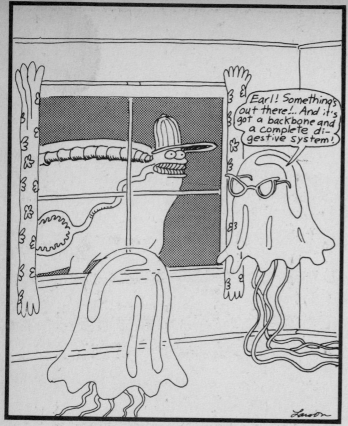

Life in the primordial soup

"Well, we've done everything we can; now we can only wait and see if she pulls through. ... If she doesn't, however, I got dibs on these ribs right here."

Karl Malden in his basement

Cowmen Miranda

Moses as a kid

"So then I says to Borg, 'You know, as long as we're under
siege, one of us oughta moon these Saxon dogs.'"

Suddenly, Dr. Morrissey's own creation, a hideous creature nine feet tall and bearing the heads of the Brady Bunch, turns against him.

Early settlers of Beverly Hills

Slowly he would cruise the neighborhood, waiting for that
occasional careless child who confused him
with another vendor.

Construction birds at lunch

More Facts of Nature: As part of nature's way to help spread the species throughout their ecological niche, bison often utilize a behavior naturalists have described as "ballooning."

Early kazoo bands

Anatidaephobia: The fear that somewhere, somehow, a duck is watching you.

Tethercat

"Just look at this room — body segments everywhere!"

The matador's nightmare

Primitive fraternities

"I don't know if this is such a wise thing to do, George."

"You know, Vern... the thought of what this place is gonna look like in about a week just gives me the creeps."

"Yo! Everyone down there! This is the jackal! I'm tired of slinking around in the shadows! ... I'm coming down to the kill! Is that gonna be cool with everyone! ... I don't want trouble!"

"Careful, Lyle! ... There's some cattle dancing!"

"Did you detect something a little ominous in the way they said, 'See you later'?"

"I tell you I've *had* it! ...I'm not climbing into that getup one more time until you tell me why I'm always the *back* end!"

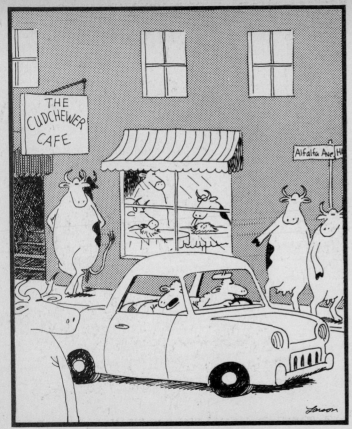

"Drive, Ted! We've stumbled into some cowtown."

"*Sure* it's true! ... Cross my heart and hope to die, stick a sharp chunk of obsidian in my eye."

The Potatoheads in Brazil

Bombardier beetles at home

"We understand your concern, ma'am — but this just isn't enough for us to go on. Now, you find the *other* half of your husband, and then we've got a case."

Mobile hobbyists

How the human egg is often deceived.

Frog pioneers

"Aha! The murderer's footprints!
'Course, we all leave tracks like this."

"Hey! Ernie Wagner! I haven't seen you in, what's it been — 20
years? And hey — you've still got that thing growin' outta your
head that looks like a Buick!"

"Good heavens, Bernie! We've got company! ...
And you're never going to catch that stupid squirrel anyway!"

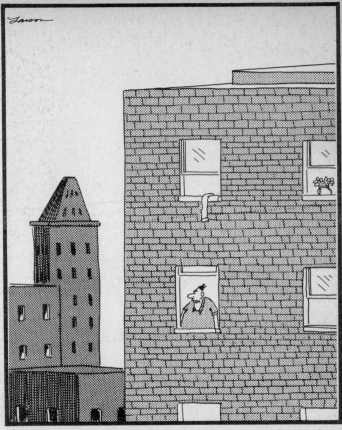

On a clear day, Eugene rose and looked around him and,
regrettably, saw who he was.

Headhunter hutwarming

"Oh, good heavens, no, Gladys — not for me.
... I ate my young just an hour ago."

Nonunion wagon masters

"Oooooooweeeeee! This thing's been here a loooooooooong time. Well, thank God for ketchup."

"OK, when I say 'draw,' we draw. ... Ready? ... One, two, three — STRAW! ... OK, just checkin' your ears. ... One, two, three — CLAW! ... OK, DRAWbridge! ..."

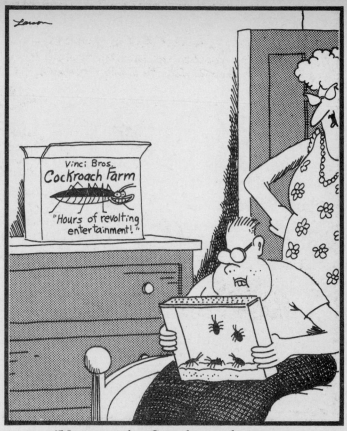

"Now remember, Cory, show us that you can take good care of these little fellows and maybe *next* year we'll get you that puppy."

Splattered with juice and hooting excitedly, Neanderthals are depicted here as they proceed to carve up their favorite kill, the woolly watermelon.

Hell's Cafeteria

Scene from *Return of the Nose of Dr. Verlucci*

Why people named Buddy hate to drive

"What? You're just going to throw the tail away? ... Why, in *my* day, we used every goldang *part* of a mammoth!"

The Fullertons demonstrate Sidney's trick knee.

Sucker fish at home

As the cactus stood watch over the sun-drenched land, a red-tailed hawk hung motionless in the desert sky. Little stirred, except an occasional lizard scurrying for shade or a tumblenerd drifting by.

"Why, thank you. ... Thank you very much!"

"I can't believe it! This is impossible! Nothing here but — wait!
Wait! I see something! ... Yes! There they are — granola bars!"

"Hold it right there, young lady! Before you go out, you take off some of that makeup and wash off that gallon of pheromones!"

Street physicians

Embedded in Styrofoam "shoes," Carl is sent to
"sleep with the humans."

"I built the forms around him just yesterday afternoon when he fell asleep, and by early evening I was able to mix and pour."

"Pretty cool, Dewey. ... Hey! Shake the jar and see if they'll fight!"

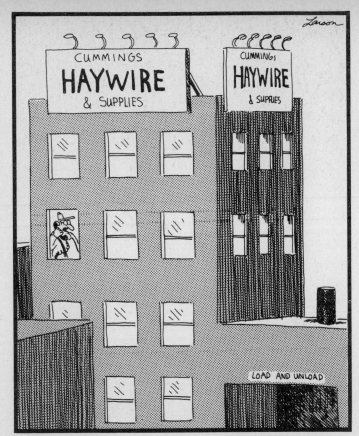

"Mr. Cummings? This is Frank Dunham in Production. ...
We've got some problems. Machine No. 5 has jammed, several
of the larger spools have gone off track, the generator's blown,
and, well, everything seems to be you-know-what."

Infamous moments in jazz

"Well, thank God we all made it out in time.
... 'Course, now we're equally screwed."

"Hey, Bob...did I scare you or what?"

"Bobby, jiggle Grandpa's rat so it looks alive, please."

"So...they tell me you're pretty handy with a gun."

Mountain families

Hummingbirds on vacation

Fruitcakes of the World

Butterfly yearbooks

"Oh, for heaven's sake, Miss Carlisle! ...
They're only cartoon animals!"

Primitive think tanks

Fly travelogues

Her answer off by miles, Sheila's "cow sense" was always a
target of ridicule.

The famous "Mr. Ed vs. Francis the Talking Mule" debates

Scene from *Bring 'Em Back Preserved*

Goldfish laundry days

Miserable little monsters.

"Yeah, yeah, buddy, I've heard it all before: You've just metamorphosed and you've got 24 hours to find a mate and breed before you die. ... Well, get lost!"

"All right! Hand me the tongs, Frank. ... We got us a big den of rattlers here."

Aladdin's lamp, end table, and sofa

Monster jobs

"You and Fred have such a lovely web, Edna —
and I *love* what you've done with those fly wings."

Professor Feldman, traveling back in time, gradually succumbs to the early stages of nonculture shock.

"The wench, you idiot! Bring me the *wench!*"

"Well, this may not be wise on a first date, but I just gotta try your garlic wharf rats."

The world was going down the tubes. They needed a scapegoat. They found Wayne.

"Well, the Sullivans are out on their tire again."

"Hold it! There's a car across the street — you sure
you weren't followed, Mary?"

"Well! No wonder! ... Look who's been loose the whole evening!"

"And this report just in. ... Apparently, the grass *is* greener on the other side."

Cockroach nightmares

The toaster divers of Pago Pago

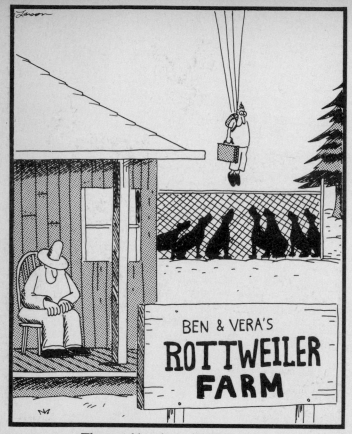

The untold ending of D.B. Cooper

Robby works his ant farm.

"You want me to stop the car, Larry, or do you want to take your brother off the rack this instant?"

An instant later, both Professor Waxman and his time machine are obliterated, leaving the cold-blooded/warm-blooded dinosaur debate still unresolved.

Michelangelo's father

Saloon scenes on other planets

Full moon and empty head

"Now relax. ... Just like last week, I'm going to hold the cape up for the count of 10. ... When you start getting angry, I'll put it down."

Edgar Allan Poe in a moment of writer's block

The elephant man meets a buffalo gal.

The big-lipped dogs of the equatorial rain forest

Young Victor Frankenstein stays after school.

"Let go, Morty! Let go, Morty! You're pulling me in!
... Let go, Morty! You're pulling me in!"

"Well, it's cold again."

"What the? ... This is lemonade! Where's my culture of amoebic dysentery?"

"Man, this is havin' no effect. ... But if the boss wants this varmint dragged through the desert, I ain't gonna argue."

"Well, well — another blond hair. ... Conducting a little more
'research' with that Jane Goodall tramp?"

"Not bad, but you guys wanna see a *really* small horse?"

"No, no, no! What are you doing? ... Fifth leg! Fifth leg!"

"That does it, Sid. ... You yell 'tarantula' one more time and you're gonna be wearin' this thing."

And by coincidence, Carl had just reached the "m's."

Early archaeologists

Crossing paths on their respective
journeys of destiny, Johnny Appleseed and
Irving Ragweed nod "hello."

Roger crams for his microbiology midterm.

"Tell it again, Gramps! The one about being caught in the shark frenzy off the Great Barrier Reef!"

When dogs go to work

Accountant street gangs

Just when you thought it was safe to go back into the topsoil.

The fake McCoys

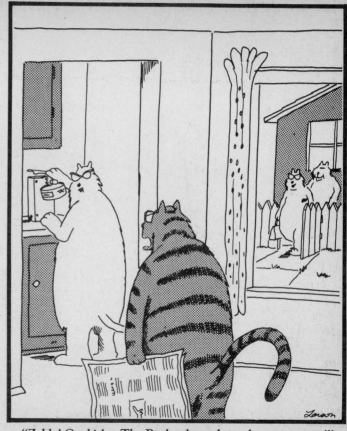

"Zelda! Cool it! ... The Rothenbergs hear the can opener!"

Inexplicably, Bob's porcupine goes flat.

"Carl, maybe you should just leave your flashlight off. We're trying to scare these kids, not crack 'em up."

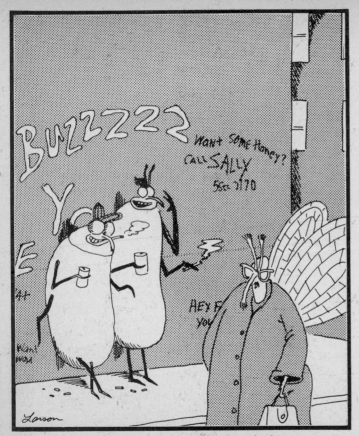

Killer bees are generally described
as starting out as larvae delinquents.

The spitting cobras at home

Thor's hammer, screwdriver, and crescent wrench

"I had them all removed last week and, boy, do I feel great."

Early piñatas

"Hey, everyone! Simmons here just
uttered a discouraging word!"

"Letter from Lonso. ... And he sounds pretty lonely."

"Man, Ben, I'm gettin' tired of this. ... How many days now we've been eatin' this trail dust?"

Although skilled with their pillow arsenal, the Wimpodites were favorite targets of Viking attacks

Stephen King's childhood ant farm

"Egad! It's Professor DeArmond — the epitome of evil amongst butterfly collectors!"

Trick clubbing exhibitions

"Well, look who's excited to see you back from being declawed."

"Aaaaaaaaaaaaa! Earl! ...
We've got a poultrygeist!"

"Mom! ... Earl's grossing me out with a mouthful of worms!"

At the hospital for mothers whose children stepped on sidewalk cracks

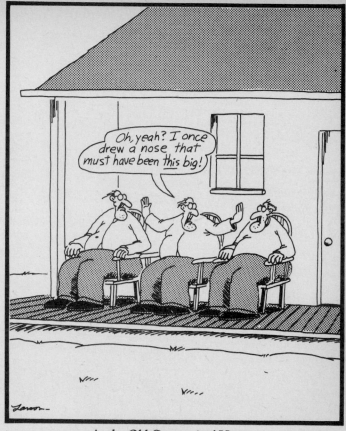

At the Old Cartoonists' Home

Futura now offers an exciting range of quality fiction and non-fiction by both established and new authors.
All of the books in this series are available from good bookshops, or can be ordered from the following address:

Futura Books
Cash Sales Department
P.O. Box 11
Falmouth
Cornwall, TR10 9EN.

Please send cheque or postal order (no currency), and allow 60p for postage and packing for the first book plus 25p for the second book and 15p for each additional book ordered up to a maximum charge of £1.90 in U.K.

B.F.P.O. customers please allow 60p for the first book, 25p for the second book plus 15p per copy for the next 7 books, thereafter 9p per book.

Overseas customers, including Eire, please allow £1.25 for postage and packing for the first book, 75p for the second book and 28p for each subsequent title ordered.